The spacecraft stood on its launching pad.
Excitement filled the air!
The astronauts marched in a parade
As crowds were gathering there.

1

The people cheered and waved their flags
As the astronauts entered in
And made last minute checks on board.
The countdown would begin!

2

Their "lift-off" was spectacular,
A sight above all sights!
The spacecraft rose with a thrilling roar,
Ascending to the heights.

The craft reached space, then leveled off.
Its orbiting began.
It seemed suspended over Earth
In perfect calm, but then—

A meteor shower! The craft was bounced
And tossed from side to side.
The astronauts took strong control
To stabilize their ride.

They kept their craft upon its c...
This trouble soon would pass.
When all was clear, the hatch was opened.
The team "space-walked" at last!

They ...cked the craft for damages,
...one were to be found!
They went back in to start descent
To bring the craft back down.

They made a perfect landing,
Their mission over at last.
The astronauts stepped from their craft.
Crowds cheered as they marched past!